Disney

101 DALMATIANS

Candid Puppy Shots

DRAW YOUR FAVORITE DALMATIAN PUPPY.

DRAW A PICTURE

WADDLESWORTH IS DAYDREAMING ABOUT A BONE. WHAT DO YOU DAYDREAM ABOUT?

UNSCRAMBLE

UNSCRAMBLE THESE 102 DALMATIAN WORDS.

LELAURC ....

GBI NEB ....

GSOD ....

TRLEHSE ....

TOAC ....

SNAMNOI ....

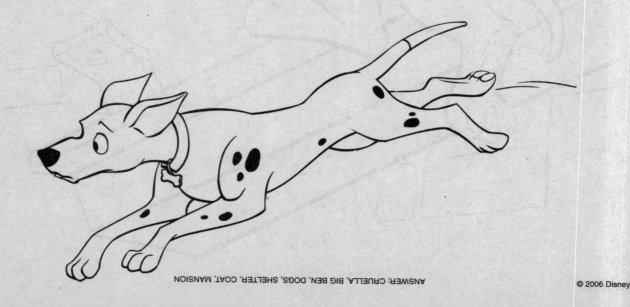

How many times can you find the word:

BARK

A B A R K B R
B A R K K B K
B R K B A R K
A K A R B R A
R R K R A B B
K R A B A B A
R K R A B A R
A R A B A R K
B A R K A K K

Look every direction.
Circle each word as you go.
Your answer _____.

How many dogs do you count?

PAWS FOR THOUGHT

SAVE THE DOGS

Help the cab take Kevin to his home.

DECODE

Use these symbols to decode the name of a shelter.

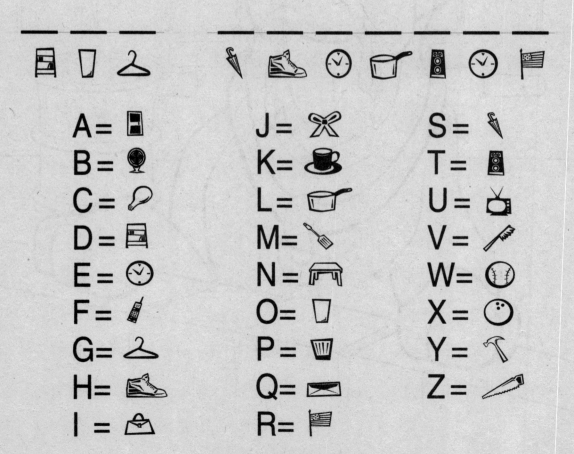

Roger Radcliffe was a musician who lived
in London with his Dalmatian dog, Pongo.

WHICH PONGO IS DIFFERENT?

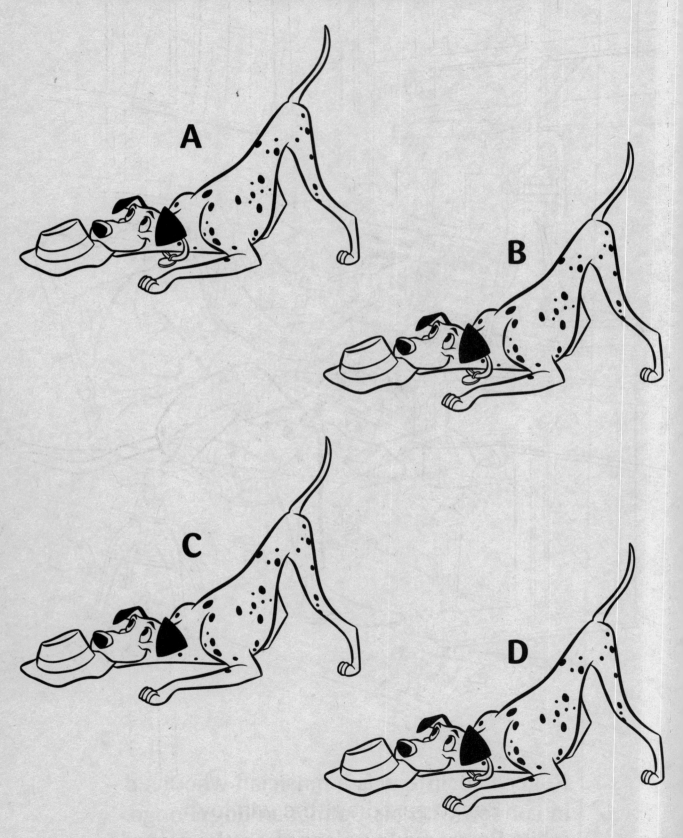

A

B

C

D

ANSWER: C

Pongo gazed out the window
while Roger made up songs on the piano.

WORD SEARCH

Look up, down, across and diagonally for these words:

LONDON	BARK	SPOTS
PONGO	TIBS	CRUELLA	SOOT
PERDITA	ESCAPE	PUPPIES	HOME

```
M L J D K W I C Q M K Y
S P O T S J V Q P D R U
H L B N I E D K O A A Q
C J Q P D B K L N J B S
P R P Y O O S J G H G O
E A U C V E N A O K A O
R I B E J N Z P H E F T
D K J A L P U P P I E S
I H S M Q L V B H O M E
T M N L N T A Q J U Z E
A D P E S C A P E Q G J
```

He saw a little Pekingese riding in the basket of a bicycle...

...and a fancy poodle prancing down the street.

Wait! There was a lady and her beautiful Dalmatian!

"They're headed for the park," thought Pongo.

HELP PONGO FIND HIS WAY TO THE LADY DALMATIAN IN THE PARK.

FINISH

START

In the park, Roger and Pongo strolled by Anita
and her sweet Dalmatian, Perdita.

It was fun to snatch Roger's hat!

Pongo tangled his leash around Roger and Anita.

Roger's hat took a dunking.

**Roger and Anita fell into the pond.
Then they fell in love!**

SPOT THE DIFFERENCE!

Can you spot the 5 differences between the top picture and the bottom one?

ANSWERS: Roger's pipe, Anita's belt, Roger's shoes, Pongo's spots, and Perdita's leash.

Roger married Anita, and Pongo wed
the beautiful Dalmatian, Perdita.

Roger was so happy he twirled Anita around
their little house.

Pongo found out he was going to be a father!
Perdita was having puppies!

"The puppies are here!" said Nanny.
"And there are 15 of them!"

Cruella De Vil wanted to buy the puppies.
"We're not selling the puppies!" Roger shouted

The puppies liked to crowd around the television set before being tucked into bed.

WHICH PIECE COMPLETES THE PICTURE?

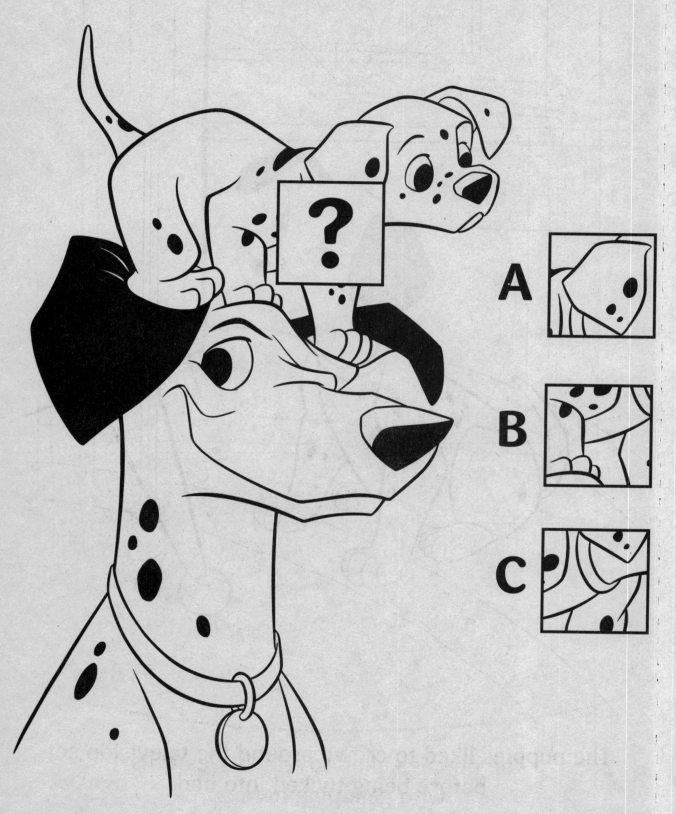

The puppies liked to watch Westerns
with galloping horses.

The Radcliffes walked Pongo
and Perdy in the park every day.

A tall, thin man named Jasper and his brother,
Horace, plotted to steal the puppies for Cruella De Vil.

The evil men got into the house by pretending
to be from the electric company.

Horace and Jasper locked Nanny in a room upstairs.

"The puppies! They took the puppies!" Nanny cried.

Cruella was thrilled to hear the puppies were missing.

MATCH EACH PUPPY TO ITS SHADOW.

Dogs all over London spread the word
through the Twilight Bark.

News about the missing puppies went
from rooftops to pet shops.

The all-dog alert spread from the city streets to the country.

The Colonel, an old English sheepdog, heard the news.
He told Sergeant Tibs the cat, and the Captain, a horse.

"I heard barking at the old De Vil mansion," reported Tibs.

Sergeant Tibs and the Colonel went to investigate.

HELP THE MESSAGE REACH THE COLONEL.

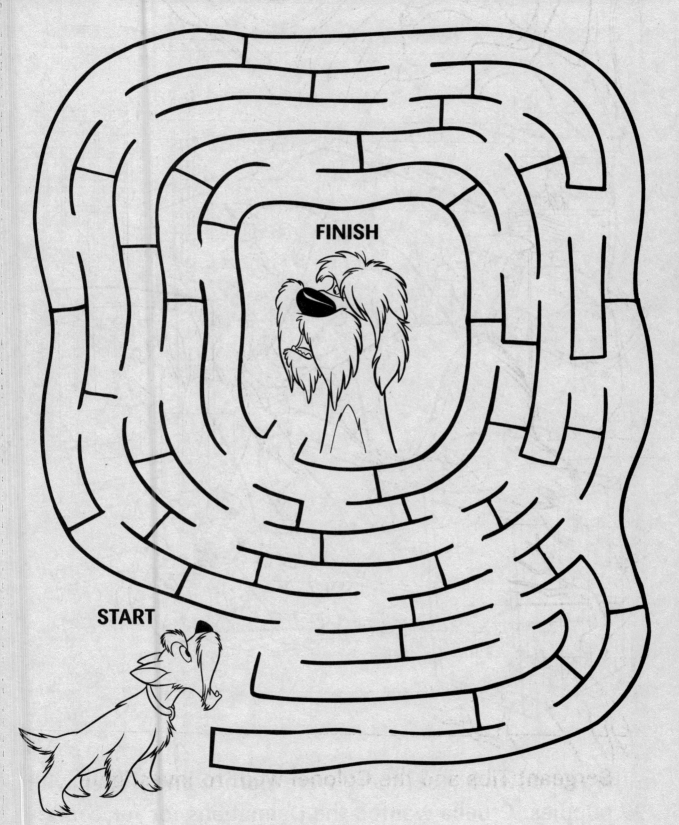

FINISH

START

In the run-down house, there were Horace and Jasper with
99 puppies. Cruella wanted the Dalmatians for fur coats!

When Horace and Jasper made their rounds,
Tibs helped the puppies crawl through a hole in the wall.

The brave cat was attacked
by the dognappers—but escaped!

Pongo and Perdita hid the puppies
in an old blacksmith's shop.

Cruella's roadster swerved out of control,
rammed into Jasper's truck, and crashed in the snow.

Cruella's henchmen were no match for 101 Dalmatians!

Perdy joyfully told Anita they were safe at home at last.

Roger and Pongo did a little dance.

HOW MANY DALMATIANS DO YOU COUNT?

Nanny dusted soot off all the puppies.

Roger and Anita decided to keep all the puppies
and have a Dalmatian Plantation!

How is Oddball different from the other puppies?

Use these symbols to decode the answer.

WHICH PICTURE OF CRUELLA IS DIFFERENT?

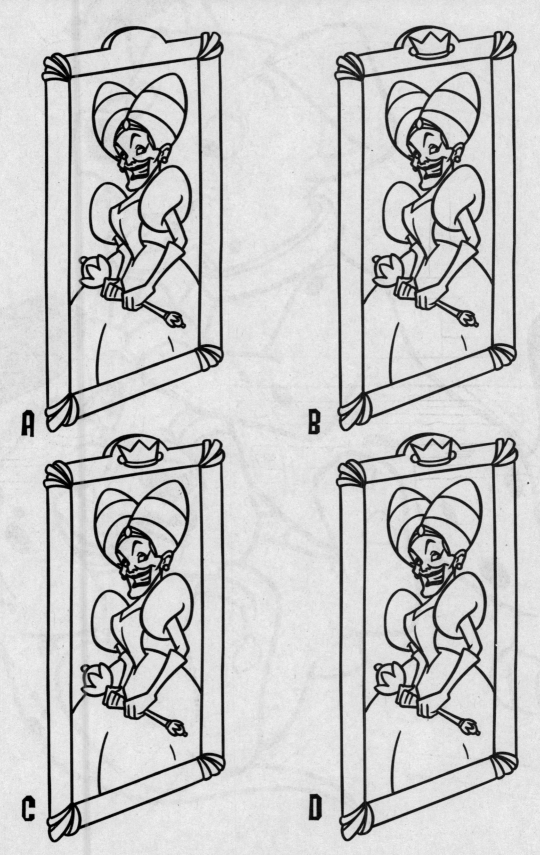

A

B

C

D

CROSSWORD

Finish this puzzle by using the names on this list.

ALONSO   CRUELLA
PAVLOV   CHLOE
BUTTON   KEVIN
WADDLESWORTH   AGNES

WHICH ONE OF THESE PICTURES DOES NOT BELONG?

A

B

C

D

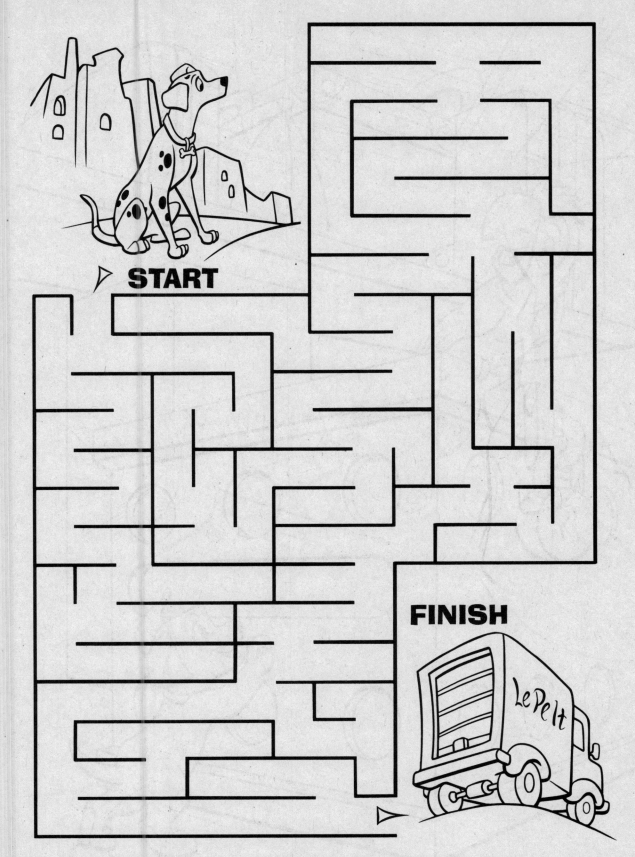

START

FINISH

Le Pelt

Help Dipstick find LePelt's Truck.

How many times can you find the word:

BONE

```
B B O N E E E
B O N E B N N
E N O B O E N
N E B B O N E
O B O N E O N
B O N E B B O
O N E N O E B
N E B O N E E
E N O B E N O
```

Look every direction.
Circle each word as you go.
Your answer _____.

ODDBALL DOESN'T
HAVE ANY SPOTS.
DRAW THEM
ON HER.

DRAW

Follow the maze to spell
what Oddball really wants?

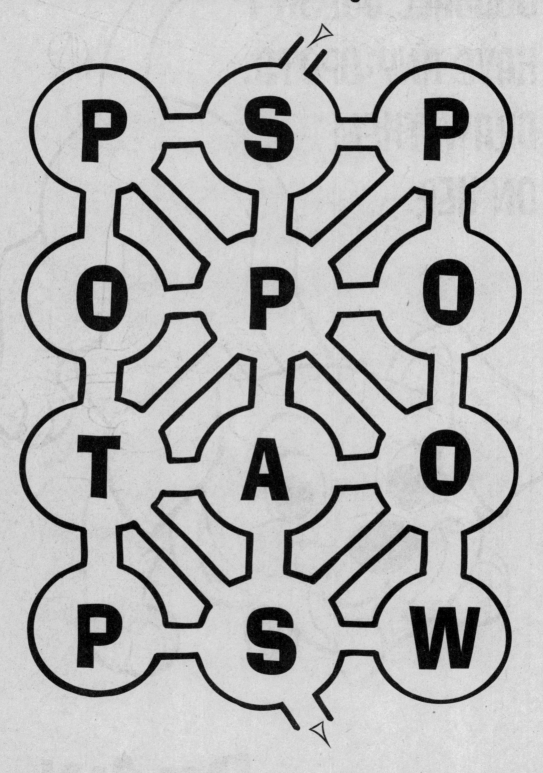

_ _ _ _ _ _ _ _

UNSCRAMBLE

TO MAKE A CRUELLA CAKE
YOU MAY NEED THESE INGREDIENTS.

RLFOU ....

GSGE ....

LKIM ....

AECLRLU ....

TETUBR ....

GARUS ....

MATCH EACH PUP TO ITS PORTRAIT.